MORE SCARY STORY STARTERS

By Julie Koerner

Illustrated by Kerry Manwaring

LOWELL HOUSE JUVENILE

LOS ANGELES

NTC/Contemporary Publishing Group

For Jenna and Matt
—J.K.

Managing Director and Publisher: Jack Artenstein
Director of Publishing Services: Rena Copperman
Editorial Director, Juvenile: Brenda Pope-Ostrow
Director of Juvenile Development: Amy Downing
Director of Art Production: Bret Perry
Editor: Jessica Oifer
Designer: Lisa-Theresa Lenthall

Lowell House books can be purchased at special discounts when
ordered in bulk for premiums and special sales.
Contact Customer Service at:
NTC/Contemporary Publishing Group, Inc.
4255 W. Touhy Avenue, Lincolnwood, Illinois 60646-1975 U.S.A.
1-800-323-4900

ISBN: 1-56565-766-7

Printed and bound in the United States of America

10 9 8 7 6 5 4

note to parents

For those children who love a good scare—and who love to scare others—**MORE SCARY STORY STARTERS** is a workbook that will promote both creativity and enjoyment. It contains a strong mix of creative writing and storytelling exercises. While each exercise is enhanced by black-line drawings, in some cases your child is encouraged to do his or her own spooky illustrations.

Remember that children who do not yet have the language and spelling skills necessary to write full, "correct" sentences are more than capable of expressing their ideas phonetically and need to be challenged to do so.

Throughout **MORE SCARY STORY STARTERS,** story "skeletons" are provided for your child to "flesh" out. Please work with your child and encourage him or her to do the exercises in order. This will help the child to go on to write full, complete stories. Your child should first finish the fill-in-the-blank sentences by choosing words from provided lists, or by choosing words of his or her own. Then, for several writing exercises, your child is asked to write the beginning, middle, or end of a terrifying tale, thereby learning valuable information on the art of sequential storytelling. Your child will discover the distinctions between these three parts of a story and the unique role each plays in telling a *good* ghostly story.

Designed to promote fun, creativity, and self-confidence, and develop such skills as language arts, storytelling, sequential relationships, logic, reasoning, and lots more, **MORE SCARY STORY STARTERS** is sure to be a success with you and your child.

you make the monster!

What is scary to you? Something that is scary to one person might not be scary to someone else. Show the difference between what you think is scary and what is *not* scary. The pictures on the next two pages are exactly the same. Follow the directions to make one monster scary and one monster silly.

The Scary Monster

1. Give this monster big scary eyes.
2. Put a horrifying hat on its head.
3. Make this monster's mouth look scary.
4. Draw creepy clothing on its body.
5. Give this monster frightening fingers.
6. Draw scary shoes or boots on its feet.
7. Put a spooky nose and icky ears on this monster.
8. Add any other frightening features to make your monster look scary.

My scary monster's name is _____.

The Silly Monster

1. Give this monster funny-looking eyes.

2. Put a silly hat on its head.

3. Make this monster's mouth look happy.

4. Draw goofy-looking clothes on this monster.

5. Give this monster crazy fingers.

6. Draw silly shoes or boots on its feet.

7. Put a ridiculous nose and odd ears on this monster.

8. Add any other funny features to make your monster look silly.

My silly monster's name is _____.

scary or not scary?

Writers use certain words to make their stories scary. Read the sentences on this page. Circle the phrase below each sentence to tell if you think the words in the sentence make it **scary** or **not scary**.

1. Arthur walked home in a pounding rainstorm.

    scary   **not scary**

2. He passed a huge growling dog with large sharp teeth.

    scary   **not scary**

3. "Hello, Bowser," Arthur said with a big friendly smile.

    scary   **not scary**

4. Suddenly, a loud boom of thunder crashed overhead.

    scary   **not scary**

Finish the picture to show Arthur walking home from school. Be sure to show what happens after the thunder crashes overhead.

make more scary words

Now *you* write the word that will make each of these sentences scary! You may choose words from the Word Box or use words of your own.

Spagglepopple is a huge _____. When it walks,

the _____ shakes. Its foot is as big as a _____.

Spagglepopple sleeps in a _____ bed. It loves to eat

_____. When it _____, look out!

WORD BOX

elf	growls	screeches	ground
monster	sneezes	tremendous	humans
earth	spaghetti	bones	car

Draw a picture of what you think Spagglepopple looks like.

DRAWN BY _____

make it scary!

Read each short story on this page and the next. Then choose the ending you like best. Remember to make the short stories scary! Write the letter of the ending you choose on the line following each story.

Uri and Marta sat on a huge rock. They looked at the ocean below. It was a quiet, peaceful day. Suddenly, a large dark shadow started to move under the water! It came closer to the rock where Uri and Marta sat.

Then it came to the surface! It was _____

A. a mass of seaweed!

B. a sea monster!

C. a giant piranha!

The wind howled outside Susan's window. It was so noisy! It slammed a tree branch against the side of the house. Her doors and windows rattled. Susan heard a sound from far away. *Waaaaaa, waaaaaa, waaaaaa,* went the sound. She tried to ignore it, but the sound just wouldn't stop. Finally, Susan went to her window and saw _____

A. a ghost floating in the air.

B. a stray cat.

C. that the wind was blowing through a crack in the glass.

It was late when Nick left school after his basketball game. He took a shortcut through the woods between the school and his home. It was dark, but Nick knew the way. He stayed on the footpath. But soon he heard a rustling noise and then a crunch. Something was between the trees. Nick walked faster. Then he saw the noisemaker, _____

A. an angry gorilla that had escaped from the zoo.

B. a ferocious monster.

C. an eight-foot-long python.

Knock, knock. The sound startled Belinda. She was baby-sitting for the Rothenbergs and was not expecting anyone.

Knock, knock, knock. Someone was at the door.

Knock, knock, knock. The sound would not stop. Quietly, Belinda tiptoed to the door. She peeked out of the peephole. She didn't see anything. As she slowly cracked open the door, _____

A. the cat leaped into the house, its hair standing on end.

B. an evil goblin tried to grab her.

C. a sudden gust of wind knocked her right off her feet.

Read the scary story below. Use a word from the Word Lists on the next page to fill in each blank.

Dr. Mixup's Invention

By _____

Dr. Mixup has quite a reputation in Blankville, where she lives. Everyone in town thinks she is one _____ doctor,
₁
all because of one of her most _____ experiments. Dr.
₂
Mixup spent many _____ working on this experiment.
₃
What did she invent? A _____ robot! The robot's face
₄
looks like a _____. Dr. Mixup made its legs just like
₅
_____ legs. It can _____ like a tiger. When Dr. Mixup
₆ ₇
and her robot walk down the street, everyone _____!
₈

Draw a picture of Dr. Mixup's robot in the space below.

WORD LISTS

1. wacky, scary, weird, strange, spooky, smart, clever, happy, creepy

2. unusual, important, freaky, outrageous, awful, delightful, dangerous, frightening

3. weeks, months, hours, days, nights, years, minutes

4. funny, clumsy, villainous, mean, evil, gigantic, silver, human

5. clown, dog, moon, giant, panda, ghost, alien, monster, Tyrannosaurus rex

6. human, horse, chair, monster, frog, giraffe, table, crocodile

7. run, eat, growl, sleep, chew, bite, snarl, snore

8. runs, stares, screams, cries, scatters, watches, laughs, melts

another scary invention

Dr. Mixup is working on a new invention. What could she be creating? You decide. Draw a picture of her new invention. Then complete the sentences to tell about what she has invented.

DRAWN BY _____

Dr. Mixup tried to make a _____. Instead, she invented a _____. It looks like a _____. I hope it doesn't _____! I think I'll call this invention _____.

Use your own words to complete the story below. Make the story as scary as you can!

Marvin's Scary Birthday Bash

By _____

Even though Marvin's birthday is not in the month of _____, he decided to have a scary birthday party. On the invitation he wrote, "Dress as your favorite _____." Marvin wanted his apartment to look _____. He hung _____ over the doors. He covered all the windows with _____. Even his dog, _____, looked spooky. For refreshments, Marvin served _____ and _____. With a little help from his mom, Marvin _____ his own costume. He used _____ and _____. All of his friends _____ when they saw Marvin in his costume.

make it sound scary!

Did you know that certain words can make something sound scarier? These words are describing words, also called **adjectives**. Match the describing words on the left to the **nouns** (which are people, places, or things) on the right to make them sound SCARY.

hairy	teeth
spiked	tiger
sharp	shark
roaring	haircut
mean	toad
ferocious	ghost
ugly	alligator
spooky	goblin
scary	sound
frightful	storm

Some of these words would sound funny if you put them together. Have you ever heard of "hairy teeth"? Make some of your own funny combinations using the words above.

_____   _____

_____   _____

_____   _____

_____   _____

scary similes

When writers compare one thing to something else, they create a simile. A **simile** is a comparison that uses the words **like** or **as**. Look at this example: **The vampire's teeth were as sharp as knives.**

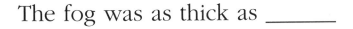

Choose the phrase that best completes each scary simile. Write the letter of that phrase on the blank line at the end of the simile.

The fog was as thick as _____

A. a blanket.

B. a cloud.

C. pea soup.

Robert's shadow was huge, like a _____

A. house.

B. Tyrannosaurus rex.

C. people-eating monster.

Ms. Meany's stew was as hot as _____

A. red pepper.

B. coal.

C. a dragon's fiery breath.

make your own creepy comparisons

Now use your imagination to write some scary similes of your own!

The coyote looked as hungry as a _____.

Some people think Ms. Meany is as spooky as a _____.

The raindrops sounded like _____ on the roof.

Bryan's story was as scary as a _____.

The tiger growled, showing teeth as sharp as _____.

It was as dark as _____ in the cave.

The thunder sounded like _____ in the sky.

Jennifer's science experiment smelled as strong as _____.

story order

Every good story needs a beginning, a middle, and an end. The **beginning** tells readers what the story is about. The **middle** tells the problem, or plot. The problem is solved in the **end**.

Look at the two stories told in pictures below. Put each story in order by writing **beginning, middle,** or **end** under the correct pictures.

_____   _____   _____

_____   _____   _____

story order

Put the spooky story below in the correct order by writing **beginning, middle,** or **end** on the line below each part.

The Noise

Mark's dad picked up a flashlight. Together, they slowly opened the basement door and tiptoed down the stairs. Scratch, scratch. They heard it again. Mark's dad pointed his flashlight at the noise. Suddenly, what looked like a huge, sharp-toothed rat jumped out at them.

_____

It landed on Mark's arm. He screamed, and his dad batted the rat away with the flashlight. All was quiet. Mark's dad turned the flashlight toward the ground. The ratlike creature was nowhere to be found. Mark and his dad slowly walked back upstairs to clean Mark's wound.

_____

One night, Mark heard a strange noise coming from the basement. Scratch, scratch, scratch. Mark went to his dad. "Dad," he said, "there's a weird sound in the basement."

_____

Put the spooky story below in the correct order by writing **beginning, middle,** or **end** on the line below each part.

Mrs. O'Malley Is Missing

Finally, Principal Houser entered the classroom. "I'll have to take over today," she explained to the somewhat startled kids. "Mrs. O'Malley . . . well . . . she had to go away last night." Principal Houser smiled a sinister smile.

_____

The morning bell rang. All the kids in Mrs. O'Malley's class took their seats. Then they waited.

_____

Something was very odd. Mrs. O'Malley was not in her place at the front of the classroom. They had no teacher. The kids began to squirm and whisper. They wondered, "Where's Mrs. O'Malley?"

_____

Complete the story below by writing the missing sentences.

The Mystery of Bones

By _____

Maria was worried about her cat, Bones. He had been missing for two days, and a bad storm was brewing.

Maria had looked everywhere for Bones. She hoped Bones wasn't lost or hurt outside in the storm.

_____

_____

_____

_____

_____

Complete the story below by writing the missing sentences.

Mystery Stew

By _____

When George got home from school, he found a note from his mother. Her handwriting looked strange. The note said, "I have to work late tonight. I left a pot of 'mystery' stew on the stove for your dinner. Warm it up very carefully. Love, Mom."

George looked at the overflowing pot on the stove. He started to walk toward it and then stopped. Had his mom really made that stew?

Use the pictures on this page and the next to write the story.

The Haunted House

By _____

_____

_____

_____

_____

_____

_____

_____

Use the pictures to write the story below.

A Smart Call?

By _____

_____
_____
_____
_____
_____

_____
_____
_____
_____
_____

_____
_____
_____
_____
_____

On the next few pages, the beginnings and middles of spooky stories have been written for you. You write the ending to tell what happens.

The Umbrella Jinx

By _____

"**H**ow are you feeling?" Laura asked Janie. She handed Janie some books and cards from her friends at school. Janie was on her bed. Her leg was in a cast.

"Great, if you don't count this broken leg," grumbled Janie. She was pretty uncomfortable.

"Exactly how did it happen?" Laura asked.

"Remember the rain we had two nights ago?" Janie asked. "I was walking Merlin and holding that umbrella." She pointed to a red umbrella in the corner of her room. "I didn't see a car that was coming around the corner. It splashed water on me, and I jumped backward. Then I tripped on the curb and fell."

"Sounds like bad luck," Laura said, sitting carefully on the edge of Janie's bed.

"I think that umbrella blocked my vision," Janie said, casting a dirty look at the red umbrella. "I think it's jinxed. Since it's raining, you take it. It brought me bad luck."

"I don't believe an object can be jinxed," Laura said. "But if it will make you feel better, I'll take it."

Laura carried the red umbrella home. When she approached her front door, she looked around for her cat.

"Satin, I'm home," she called. Laura's cat always greeted her outside. Satin came around the corner of the house to say hello to Laura, but when the cat saw the red umbrella, she jumped! Satin raced off down the street.

"Satin, come back!" Laura called. She still had the umbrella in her hand.

"Maybe Janie was right about this umbrella," thought Laura. "Maybe it *is* jinxed, or maybe even cursed." It was beginning to rain harder. Laura wasn't sure if she should use the red umbrella as she searched for Satin, but she took it anyway.

"Hi, Laura," said a voice. Travis rode his bike up to Laura and stopped. He saw her worried face. "Is something wrong?"

"Yes," Laura said. "Satin ran away when she saw this umbrella. I didn't believe it at first, but now I think this umbrella has a jinx."

"Ba-LO-ney!" said Travis. "I'll take that umbrella off your hands, and I'll find Satin."

Laura watched Travis ride down the street. She could see the red umbrella across his handlebars. But she couldn't believe what she saw next. _____

_____

_____

_____

_____

_____

_____

_____

The End

Draw a picture to illustrate your ending.

DRAWN BY _____

Write the ending to complete the story.

The Ghost of Plainberg

By _____

The town of Plainberg was *almost* the same as other towns. There was a mayor, a fire chief, and a police chief. But Plainberg had one thing no other town had. Plainberg had a ghost.

Everyone in town knew about Otto. Some people had seen him. Others had seen evidence that Otto had been there. Others had heard the stories. You see, Otto liked to play mean tricks on people.

Otto showed up in unexpected places. For example, the fourth graders in Mr. Castro's class were convinced that he showed up at their picnic at Plainberg Park.

Before lunch, Mr. Castro said, "Let's take fifteen minutes to walk around the park. Then we'll have our picnic." When they returned, all of their lunches were gone. Someone (or something) had eaten all the food and left a huge mess.

"It must have been Otto," one student said, and all the kids agreed.

Then there was the story of Mrs. Parker's beautiful flower garden. Mrs. Parker loved her flower garden. She worked in it every afternoon. One day, it was filled with big beautiful flowers. Then, the next day, her garden was full of tall ugly weeds. They had sprouted up where the flowers had been.

"Otto has been in my garden," Mrs. Parker said to herself.

But no one in Plainberg could believe what Otto did on that fateful day in July. Nobody thought he was capable of something so frightening. But how else were they to believe that _____

_____

_____

_____

_____

_____

_____

_____

The End

Write the ending to complete the story.

The House on the Hill

By _____

One Saturday morning in spring, Alex and two of his friends went hiking. They followed a path into the woods. The path led up a steep hill. Before they knew it, they had climbed uphill a really long way.

"Can we stop a minute?" asked Nick. "I need a drink of water." He opened his canteen, took a long drink, and then passed the water to Alex.

"Look!" Sarah pointed between some trees. They saw a little house made of wood.

"Let's check it out," Nick said.

"No way," Sarah said. "Someone might live in there." But Alex and Nick were already walking toward the tiny house. Sarah followed them.

The three friends walked closer to the house, which had one door and only one window. It was very dark inside, and there were no sounds coming from the house. It appeared to be empty.

"Hello," said Alex from outside the open door. "Is anyone here?" There was no answer.

Suddenly, the three friends heard an ear-piercing sound. It came from inside the house. Alex, Nick, and Sarah did not wait to find out what had made the sound. They _____

_____

_____

_____

_____

_____

_____

_____

_____

_____

_____

The End

Write the ending to complete the story.

A Ghostly Encounter

By _____

The Winkville Middle School Nature Club spent Saturday hiking through Winkville Forest. Late in the afternoon, they built a fire and cooked supper. Then they sat around the campfire and talked. Soon the conversation turned to ghosts.

"Ghosts aren't necessarily mean," said George, as if he had some personal experience with ghosts. "Sometimes they are friendly or kind."

"Imagine you could talk to the ghost of a person who once lived. Who would you choose?" asked Randall.

"I would like to talk to Abraham Lincoln's ghost," said Lindsey. "I'd ask him what life was like during the Civil War."

"I would like to talk to the ghost of Eleanor Roosevelt," said Isabelle.

"I would—" George was cut off by a loud scream coming from just a few feet away.

Everyone turned toward the sound, but there wasn't much to see. It was so dark.

Then, suddenly, _____

_____

_____

_____

_____

_____

_____

_____

_____

The End

Draw a picture to illustrate your ending.

Write the ending to complete the story.

Max's Warning

By _____

One night, at about 2:00 A.M., the Whittemores' dog began to bark.

"Max, be quiet!" said Donny, half asleep. But Max kept barking wildly.

Donny's mom opened her bedroom door. "Max! Settle down," she said. But her words didn't calm Max at all. He went to the window and barked. He went to the door and barked. He ran up the stairs. Then he ran back down the stairs.

"What is all this racket?" said Donny's dad, who was now up. He looked at Max. "What's going on, boy?" Max ran around Donny's dad in a circle.

"Do you need to go out?" he asked the dog. Donny's dad went to the front door and opened it. Max's barking got louder, but he didn't go outside.

"Maybe we're about to have an earthquake," Donny said. He was standing at the top of the stairs. "I heard that dogs can sense an earthquake before humans can."

"Well, something is disturbing him," said Donny's mom. "This isn't like Max."

Mr. Whittemore patted Max on the head. "C'mon, boy," he said to Max. "What's all this about . . . ?"

Suddenly, Max took off. He ran out the front door and down the driveway. The whole family ran after him. They ran all the way to the edge of the yard and then stopped—dead in their tracks—when they saw _____

_____

_____

_____

_____

_____

_____

_____

_____

_____

_____

_____

_____

_____

The End

On the next few pages, you will find the beginnings and endings of stories. You have to write the middles. Remember to make them scary!

A Not-So-New House

By _____

This house is a very good deal," Mr. White said. He parked his car in front of an empty house and then opened the door for the Greenes. Mrs. Greene and her two children, Matt and Jenna, got out of the car and looked toward the house.

"It is priced much lower than any other house in this neighborhood," Mr. White added.

"Why is it such a good deal?" Matt asked Mr. White.

"Well, I'll tell you, son," Mr. White said. "Some people say it is haunted. Now, we all know that's nonsense, but it makes it harder to sell the house."

"Haunted! Cool," said Jenna as Mr. White led them through the front door. It slammed behind them.

"Ahem . . . I'll open some windows. It's stuffy in here," said Mr. White. He opened two windows, then said, "Follow me, I'll show you the kitchen."

Bam, bam! Both windows slammed shut. As they entered the kitchen, the refrigerator door opened by itself. Then a little bell began to ring. Everyone looked around. It was a kitchen timer. Mr. White had to jiggle and fidget with it to turn it off.

"Not haunted, eh?" said Matt.

"Let's see the bedrooms!" Jenna said.

Mr. White led the Greene family down a hall toward the bedrooms. _____

_____

_____

_____

_____

_____

_____

_____

Mrs. Greene took a deep breath. "Well, I can see why people think this house is haunted," she said. Matt and Jenna were clutching each other. "I think we'll pass on the house."

The End

Write the middle to complete the story.

Witch or No Witch?

By _____

"There's no such thing as a witch," Mara told her friends.

"You haven't met Mrs. Mowitch," said Tiffany.

"She really is a witch," Sally agreed. "Everybody says so."

"How do you know? Does she fly around on her broom?" Mara laughed at her own joke. She noticed that her friends weren't laughing.

"You wouldn't think it was so funny if she had ever been _your_ baby-sitter!" said Jenny.

The girls were having a sleep-over at Mara's house. They planned to get up early Saturday morning to help clean up the park in their neighborhood.

"She stayed at my house for two days. My parents had to go to Grandma's," said Amy. "Mrs. Mowitch was so mean, I expected her to fly away!"

"She makes kids go to bed at seven o'clock!" said Tiffany. "Then you can hear her whispering on the phone. Her laugh is like a cackle."

"She always wears a black coat," Sally added. "It looks just like a witch's cape."

Tiffany said, "Have you noticed her long crooked fingernails? Only a witch would have fingernails like hers!"

"You are all exaggerating!" said Mara. "Lots of normal people wear black coats and have long fingernails."

"Do normal people chant all night long?" asked Jenny.

Just then, the girls heard an eerie noise. They jumped.

_____

_____

_____

_____

_____

_____

_____

Early the next morning, Mara's dad took the girls to the park.

"I will stay until you find your supervisor for the day," he told the girls.

"Girls." Their teacher, Mr. Stone, signaled to them. "Come meet your supervisor." He pointed to a lady in a black coat. "This is Mrs. Mowitch."

The girls gasped.

The End

Write the middle to complete the story.

Nightmare at the Library

By _____

Allison loved the library. She went there almost every day on her way home from school. Each day, she read a different book.

Allison had a favorite spot in the library. It was a small bench in the reference section. Allison could spend hours sitting on the bench, reading about life in Italy or animals on the Amazon River. Sometimes Allison would drift off to sleep. She would dream she actually lived in Italy or photographed the birds in the Amazon jungle.

One day, Allison was reading a story about people who turned into wolves. They were called werewolves, she read, and they attacked other people. The story said that to turn a werewolf back into a human, people had to tap the werewolf on the forehead three times and say the human's name.

Just as she turned the page, Allison felt _____

_____

_____

_____

"Allison, Allison, Allison." Someone was tapping her on the forehead. Allison opened her eyes slightly. She was drenched with sweat. She sighed. It was the librarian. "Allison, you fell asleep," she said softly. "You'd better go home. Your brother will be worried about you."

The End

Write the middle to complete the story.

The Old Bridge

By _____

In a village far away, there is a very old bridge that stands all alone. There is no longer any water under the bridge. Grass has grown all around it. The people of the village tell a legend about the old bridge.

There once was a princess who lived alone with her cruel father, the king. They lived in an isolated castle that was completely surrounded by trees. The king kept wolves outside the castle to chase away anyone who might wander near the castle grounds.

The princess was very lonely. Her only friends were the animals in the surrounding forest.

One day, a young hunter came to the forest. He raised his bow to kill a deer.

"Please do not kill the deer," the princess said. "She is my friend."

The kind hunter turned to the princess, smiled, and then lowered his bow. The princess and the hunter met in the forest every day for months, and eventually they fell in love.

The princess took the hunter to the king and said, "Father, I want to marry this hunter."

"You will never marry anyone!" cried the king in anger. Then he called his wolves to attack and kill the hunter.

The hunter ran as fast as he could into the forest. He hid there until the princess met him that night. Together, they ran toward the bridge.

As they approached it, _____

_____

_____

_____

_____

_____

_____

_____

_____

_____

That is why the bridge stands all alone today. There is no water that runs beneath it and no road that goes across it.  And the villagers would have it no other way.

The End

Write the middle to complete the story.

The Secret of Ghost Hill

By _____

Thomas Boyles put two fingers in his mouth and let out a shrill whistle. "This meeting of the Ghost-Chasers Club will come to order," he called out. "Today, we welcome Talene. Talene will become an official member—after she completes her initiation tonight."

He looked at Talene. "At midnight, you must walk to the top of Ghost Hill—alone." He held up a plastic jug. "When you reach the top, fill this jug with water from Ghost Waterfalls. Bring it to club headquarters tomorrow. Then you will be an official member."

That night, Talene dressed very warmly. She picked up the water jug and her flashlight. "Let's go, Duffy," she said. "Thomas didn't say anything about not bringing a dog."

Talene and Duffy started up Ghost Hill. It was a cloudy night. There was very little light from the moon.

All of a sudden, Talene heard a muffled voice. "Turn back," it said.

"What's that?" Talene asked out loud, but there was no answer.

"It must have been the wind," she said and kept on walking.

She heard it again, more clearly this time. "Turn back."

"Duffy, stop!" Talene called. She thought it was strange that Duffy wasn't barking. He was hiking up the hill as if nothing was unusual.

"Stay closer to me," Talene said to Duffy. As she neared the top of the hill, Talene heard it again. "Turn back. TURN BACK!"

Duffy's tail began to wag.

Then Talene saw _____

_____

_____

_____

_____

_____

_____

_____

_____

At the next meeting, Talene was given her official Ghost-Chasers Club badge and key chain. Thomas gave her something else, too. It was a tag for Duffy that said, "Official Mascot of the Ghost-Chasers Club."

The End

On the next few pages, you will find the middles and endings of stories. You have to write the beginnings. Remember to make them scary!

Mystery of the Deep

By _____

_____

_____

_____

_____

_____

_____

_____

_____

Then, one day, the sea monster awoke. It had been asleep for years. When the sea monster moved, the ocean floor shook. Boats rocked on the ocean's surface.

"Hmmm," said the sailors. "There must be a storm in the distance."

But there was no storm in the distance. It was the

sea monster, deep in the ocean.

None of the other ocean creatures recognized the sea monster. Even the whale was frightened by its size.

"Maybe it's a sea *dinosaur*," the tuna said to each other.

"Or a sea ghost," guessed an octopus.

Even the sharks were nervous. They were afraid the sea monster might attack and devour them.

"Feed me," the sea monster said in a gurgly, underwater kind of way. All the small fish scattered. Even the whale kept its distance.

"What do you eat?" it asked from far away, in case the answer was whales.

"I used to eat people," the sea monster responded. "I loved sailors, but after I had a run-in with that one . . . well, I thought he was human. But when I got him in my mouth, I felt his sharp . . . Let's just say that now I only eat plants. I will never go near another human again."

The End

Write the beginning to complete the story.

The Cave

By _____

_____

_____

_____

_____

_____

_____

_____

_____

Fred ran from the cave as fast as he could. He didn't stop running until he reached the campsite.

"Ah, buh, mmmmmeeennnn . . ." He tried to tell what he saw.

"Hold it, hold it, Fred!" said Mr. Barnes, the camp director. "Take a deep breath." He paused. "Now, can you speak a little more slowly?"

"I'll try," gasped Fred. "I heard a sound coming from a huge cave. The opening was so big, it didn't even look scary. So I went in."

"What did it sound like?" asked Billy, Fred's best friend.

"It sounded like water—running water," Fred replied. "The trickling sound made me very thirsty. I thought there might be a stream inside.

"Then, all of a sudden, I heard a loud screech. And something moved—something big! And it moved very fast. I think it was flying, andIthinkitwasflyingatme!"

"Fred!" said Mr. Barnes. "You are talking too fast again. We can't understand you! What happened next?"

"Something came flying right at me, I am sure of it!" Fred explained. "I think it was trying to chase me away."

Mr. Barnes used a gentle voice when he spoke. "It was probably a bat, or even a bird," he explained. "It may have been sleeping. *You* probably frightened *it*."

"Yeah, you may be right," said Fred reluctantly. He didn't really think so, though. He thought he had been chased out of the cave.

"I have an idea," said Billy. "Let's all go together to the cave tomorrow, with flashlights, and check it out."

"NO! I'm never going back there again!" Fred replied.

The End

Write the beginning to complete the story.

The Spell-Bound Statue

By _____

_____

_____

_____

_____

_____

_____

For the next hundred years, the eagle remained a statue that stood in the huge park in the middle of the city. Each day, many animals visited the statue. Birds perched on its wide wings to look over the city. Squirrels hid acorns under its stone claws.

Then, one day, a little boy sat at the foot of the eagle statue. He had his lunch in a little brown bag.

"Please help me," the eagle statue said to the boy.

The boy was frightened by the talking statue. He dropped his little brown bag and ran out of the park, all the way home.

But he thought about the eagle's pleading words all day and all night. The next day, he returned to the very same spot with his lunch bag. Again, he sat at the foot of the eagle.

"Please help me," the eagle statue repeated. Again, the boy was frightened, but this time he didn't run away.

"How could *I* help *you*?" asked the little boy in a meek voice.

"I only need some food to eat. Food will bring me back to life."

The little boy looked in his brown bag. There was a sandwich, an apple, and a bag of crackers. The little boy held a handful of crackers up to the statue's beak. A slight breeze swept through the park, and the crackers disappeared.

Instantly, the breeze became much stronger. The eagle statue's wings began to move slowly. At first, the little boy thought the wind had made the wings move. Then he saw that the eagle was truly coming back to life—right before his eyes!

"You have broken the spell," the eagle said to the little boy. "You have saved my life. Now I am off to get my revenge!"

Then the eagle flew away, leaving the confused boy alone in the park.

The End

Write the beginning to complete the story.

The Mysterious Mr. Wolfe

By _____

_____

_____

_____

_____

_____

_____

_____

_____

_____

_____

The whole class freaked out. They couldn't believe it.

The next day, Mr. Wolfe walked into the classroom a few minutes late. He scratched under his arms. He twitched his neck.

Finally, he said, "Today, we're going to review Chapter, grrrrrr, Chapter Twelve."

Kyle looked around at his classmates. He wondered if they noticed that Mr. Wolfe had growled.

"Grrrrrrrrrrrr, Kyle, do you have something to say?" Mr. Wolfe growled.

Kyle tried to be brave. "Mr. Wolfe, do you feel okay?"

"Of course I do, grrrrrrrrrrrr," Mr. Wolfe replied. "Why, grrrrrrrrrrrr, do you ask?"

Kyle couldn't even think straight. "Excuse me, Mr. Wolfe. I hear my mother calling."

Kyle sprinted out of Mr. Wolfe's class and never looked back.

The End

Draw a picture to illustrate your beginning.

DRAWN BY _____

Read the story below. Then fill in the missing parts to complete the story.

The Frightening Field Trip

By _____

Okay, kids," said Ms. Shannon, the third grade teacher. "Stay with your partner at all times."

The third graders took their seats on the bus that

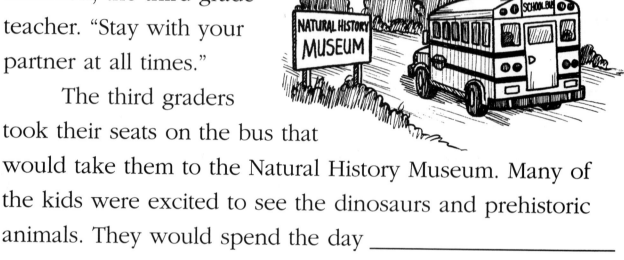

would take them to the Natural History Museum. Many of the kids were excited to see the dinosaurs and prehistoric animals. They would spend the day _____

_____

_____

_____

_____

The museum tour began in the Hall of Dinosaurs. The third graders were amazed at the size of the model dinosaurs. They looked at the real bones.

"These bones were discovered by archaeologists. Archaeologists dig in the ground to find objects that tell us about the past," said the tour guide.

ARRRRGGGGGHHHHHHHHHHHH.

All of the children turned around at once. "What was that?" someone squealed.

ARRRRGGGGGHHHHHHHHHHHHHHH. The sound came from a model of a Triceratops! Then the Triceratops's front legs started to move forward, and its head arched upward. It was alive! Instantly, the Tyrannosaurus _____

_____

_____

_____

_____

_____

_____

_____

_____

_____

_____

_____

_____

The third graders finally stopped trembling when the bus pulled into the school parking lot.

"Whew!" said Romina. "I'm glad we're home!"

The End

Write the beginning to complete the story. Then write the spell on the last page.

The Spell of the Trolls

By _____

_____

_____

_____

_____

_____

_____

_____

_____

_____

_____

_____

"All we have to do is remember the spell of the trolls, and we'll be okay," said Michael, the oldest child. "Now, let's hold hands and walk carefully through the forest."

So the four children set out to visit the Royal Kingdom. Soon they came to a thick part of the forest. They could not see the path.

They walked in carefully.

"I can't see!" It was David, the littlest child.

All of a sudden, a swarm of lightning bugs flew in front of the children. They flickered their lights so the children could see in front of them. This gave the children courage to go on.

Soon the children came to a large stream. It was too deep to swim across. It was too wide to go around.

"We're lost," said David, starting to cry.

Then, with a huge crash, a tree fell and landed straight across the stream. The children looked at the new bridge made by the tree. They looked at each other.

"We are safe now," said Michael, and they crossed the stream.

At the other side of the stream, the children found food. Fruit and berries lay at the foot of the trees. They ate and ate. Then they became very, very tired and drifted off to sleep.

"Gotcha!" Suddenly, the forest was full of goblins— evil goblins.

"Just what we wanted," they cackled, "all the children at once." And they made a circle around the children.

"Don't worry," called Susie, the second oldest child. "Just remember the spell of the trolls."

"That's right," said Michael. "Now, how did that go? *Goobledeeguppy—run like a puppy?*"

The evil goblins were surprised to hear such nonsense. But they weren't frightened. They started to laugh.

Susie gasped. "I think it's *Dinka-dinka-doo, we cast this spell on you!*" The evil goblins laughed again, even harder than before.

"I think I remember," said Melissa, one of the younger children. She began to wave her arms wildly in the air.

"*Flip, flip, spin, spin. It's the trolls' spell we've got you in.*"

Some of the goblins fell to the ground, clutching their stomachs with laughter.

"There is no spell that can save you from your fate today," said the most evil goblin of them all.

"Wait! I remember!" said David. _____

_____

_____

_____

And all of the evil goblins disappeared, never to bother little children again.

The End

Read the story below. Then write your own sentences to fill in the missing parts.

Mystery Music

By _____

This is the best vacation we've ever had!" said Amelia Galvez from the backseat of the family station wagon.

"I'm glad you think so," said Papa. The Galvez family was taking a driving vacation through the Southwest. They had driven through New Mexico, Arizona, and California. It had taken a long time. Now they were on their way home to Texas.

On their vacation, they had done many things. _____
_____
_____
_____
_____

"Papa, can we stop to hear the music?" asked little Rosa.

"What music is that?" asked Papa.

Rosa lifted her head toward the window and the sky. "That music," she replied, as if everyone could hear it.

Papa looked at Mama for an explanation.

"She's probably sleepy," said Mama. She put her arm around Rosa and pulled her close.

"Maybe she's loco," said Giancarlo, tapping the side of his forehead and looking at his sister.

"Very funny, Giancarlo," said Amelia. She was only one year older than Rosa and felt she should protect her baby sister from their teenage brother. "Maybe she's remembering a song she heard before."

"No, no," said Rosa. "*That* music. I want to see them play the music."

Even though they heard no music, everyone was quiet. They listened very hard. The only sound was the steady hum of the station wagon's engine.

_____

_____

_____

_____

_____

Rosa was starting to whimper. Mama was worried about her littlest child.

"Maybe we need to stop and stretch our legs," suggested Mama.

Papa pulled over near an abandoned house. Rosa was the first to get out of the car.

"The music!" she cried. She ran into the open door of the house.

"Wait!" yelled Mama, but Rosa was already gone.

_____

_____

_____

_____

_____

_____

_____

_____

_____

The End

Draw a picture to illustrate your ending.

Read the story on this page and the next. Then circle the ending you like best. On the last page, write an ending of your own.

The Phantom Prankster

By _____

It was a cold, windy night. Marisa was baby-sitting.

Baby-sitting for Jason was easy. He was just a baby, and he slept most of the time. So Marisa had the huge house all to herself.

Tonight was kind of spooky. The wind was whipping outside. It shook the windows and rattled tree branches against the walls. But Marisa was brave. She didn't scare easily. She sat down to watch TV.

Flash! The TV went off. "Maybe the power is out," said Marisa to herself. But the lights were still on. Marisa pushed the ON-OFF button and the TV came on again.

As Marisa watched, a magazine slid off the coffee table near her. She looked around. "How did that magazine move by itself?" she wondered out loud.

Marisa was beginning to get nervous. Suddenly, she heard a sound upstairs. It was in Jason's room. She ran upstairs to check on the baby. Jason was still asleep, but _his crib had turned halfway around!_

Marisa decided to keep Jason with her. Her hands trembled as she reached into the crib to pick him up.

Just as she began to lift Jason, his teddy bear jumped into her arms! Marisa stared at the bear. His round black eyes were staring right back at her.

Brrrrr! A shiver ran up Marisa's spine, and she dropped the bear. Very carefully, she carried Jason in her trembling arms. She walked into the kitchen. There, on the table, was a glass of milk and a piece of toast.

"Okay, who's playing these tricks on me?" Marisa said out loud. There was no answer.

"That's it. I'm calling my dad," she said to herself.

1. *Marisa picked up the phone. There was silence. The phone was dead. Marisa wrapped Jason in a blanket, hurried past the teddy bear, which was now on the couch, and ran all the way home.*

Or . . .

2. *"Don't worry, Marisa," said her dad. "I think your brother may be playing tricks on you. He said something about paying you back for talking to his girlfriend yesterday."*

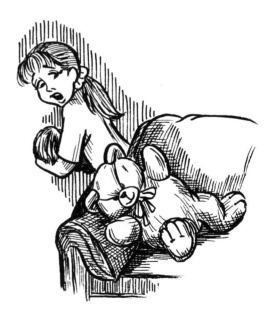

Now write your own ending here.

_____

_____

_____

_____

_____

_____

_____

_____

_____

The End

Draw a picture to illustrate your ending.

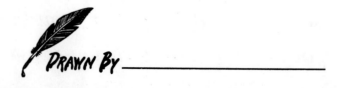

Drawn By _____